A Walk in the Country

Written by Adam and Charlotte Guillain

It was a beautiful day so Tess and Finn's family drove out of the city into the countryside. Soon, instead of buildings and traffic, they saw trees and hills.

They parked the car at the bottom of a hill and put on their boots.

"I've got the picnic," said Mum, and she patted her backpack.

"And I've got the map," said Dad.

Let's go!

Tess and Finn held on to Dylan's hands as they set off across a field.

"Look over there," whispered Tess. "There are wild rabbits running around!"

"Just like Skip!" shouted Dylan, and the rabbits scampered away.

They clambered over a stile and started to walk up the hill.

"Can I have a piggyback?" Dylan asked his dad.

"Not yet!" said Dad with a laugh. "We've only just started!"

As they walked up the hill, Dylan stopped and frowned.

"I'm tired," he moaned.

"Let's play 'I spy'," said Finn. "You go first."

"Okay," said Dylan, and he ran on ahead.

"Nice work, Finn," said Dad with a smile.

"I spy something brown!" shouted Dylan, from the top of the hill.

"Mud?" guessed Mum.

"Dad's boots?" called Tess.

"Tree trunks?" asked Finn.

Dylan shook his head.

"It was cows!" said Dylan, and he pointed down the hill to a field full of brown cows. "Race you to the bottom!" he added, as soon as the others had caught him up.

Tess and Finn chased Dylan down the slope.

At the bottom of the hill, they flopped down on the long grass and looked up at the blue sky.

"This looks like a nice shady spot for our picnic," said Mum, and she took off her backpack.

Dad put the map away and unrolled a picnic blanket for them to sit on.

Thanks!

Yum!

Mum and Dad put out the food and drink. But while everyone munched happily and gazed at the beautiful view, one of the cows was chewing on a snack too ...

When they had finished, they packed up the picnic things and set off to explore the woods.

"It's a good job we've got a map with us," said Tess. "Otherwise we might get lost in the trees."

In the woods, Finn pointed at the ground. "Look – footprints!" he said.

Tess got out her nature guide. "They're a deer's tracks!" she told them.

"You can see where they've been eating the bark of those trees," said Mum.

As they walked on, they saw squirrels nibbling nuts and heard a woodpecker hammering at a tree.

When the path split in two, Tess called, "Which way is it now, Dad?"

Dad reached into his backpack and frowned.

"Oh, dear," he muttered. "The map's gone."

Finn gulped as he saw his parents exchange a worried glance.

"A cow ate it!" said Dylan, giggling.

Dad took a deep breath and pointed. "I'm pretty sure it's this way," he said firmly.

Mum shrugged and smiled at Finn and Tess. "Okay, we're following you!" she told Dad.

On and on they walked. Tess began to get a sinking feeling in her stomach.

"Are you sure this is the right way?" she asked Dad, nervously. "I haven't seen the deer tracks we passed."

"I hope so," said Dad.

"There's the car!" said Finn. Dylan jumped up and down, and Mum gave Dad a relieved look. The whole family ran across the field towards the car …

… but stopped when they reached a stream!

"How do we get to the car?" asked Finn.

"This can't be the way we came," added Tess. Mum put down her backpack and looked at the water.

"We'll just have to cross the stream!" said Dad.

Mum frowned. "It doesn't look too deep," she said, "but we don't want to get wet."

"I've got an idea!" called Tess, pointing at some rocks.

"Stepping stones!" said Mum with a smile. "I'll put the first one in the stream and then you can pass me the others."

"Good idea!" said Dad. "I'll go last!"

They all worked together …

… and soon it was just Dad left to cross.

He began jumping from stone to stone. "This is a fun way back!" he laughed. "I'm quite glad we got lost!"

"Be careful, Dad!" said Finn.

Tess and Finn helped pull Dad out of the water.

"You can dry off in the car!" called Mum.

"A walk in the country is nice," spluttered Dad, "but shall we go back to the city now?"

Talk about the story

Answer the questions:

1 What animal did Dylan see first?

2 What game did Finn suggest they play as they walked up the hill?

3 What sort of footprints did Finn spot?

4 What does the word 'exchange' mean?

5 Why did Tess get a sinking feeling in her stomach?

6 Why was Dad happy to go back to the city at the end of the story?

7 Can you describe why the family get lost in the story?

8 Do you like going for nature walks? Why or why not?

Can you retell the story in your own words?